EARLY AMERICAN BOOKBINDINGS

EARLY AMERICAN BOOKBINDINGS

FROM THE
COLLECTION OF
Michael Papantonio

NEW YORK
The Pierpont Morgan Library
WITH
American Antiquarian Society
Cornell University Library
Princeton University Library
University of Virginia Library
1972

EXHIBITIONS

CORNELL UNIVERSITY
Olin Library, Ithaca, New York,
October 10 – November 13, 1972

UNIVERSITY OF VIRGINIA
Aldeman Library, Charlottesville, December 1–27, 1972

THE PIERPONT MORGAN LIBRARY
New York, January 11 – February 17, 1973

AMERICAN ANTIQUARIAN SOCIETY
Worcester, Massachusetts, March 5–30, 1973

PRINCETON UNIVERSITY LIBRARY
Princeton, New Jersey, April 25 – May 31, 1973

LIBRARY OF CONGRESS CATALOG CARD NUMBER 72–91710

ISBN 87598–037–6

CONTENTS

FOREWORD

THE idea for this exhibition came on the night of the last annual meeting of The Bibliographical Society of America, when a small group had gathered to see the collection. Professor Donald Eddy, Rare Books Librarian at Cornell University Library, suggested a joint "travelling exhibition." Mr. Marcus A. McCorison, Director of the American Antiquarian Society, Dr. Charles Ryskamp, Director of the Pierpont Morgan Library, William S. Dix, Librarian of Princeton University, and Mr. William H. Runge, Curator of Rare Books at the University of Virginia Library, agreed to exhibit a selection and to have an illustrated catalogue prepared.

A few bindings were purchased in the late thirties and early forties, but the acquisition in 1948 of Mrs. Emma C. Embury's handsomely bound *New York Mirror and Ladies Literary Gazette*, 1831 (no. 54) was the starting point of the collection as it now stands.

Miss Hannah D. French, now working on a revision and greatly enlarged edition of her section on "Early American Bookbinding by Hand" in *Bookbinding in America* (1941), and Carol and Willman Spawn, whose work on eighteenth-century Philadelphia binders and bindings is nearing completion, assisted in the selection of the bindings to be shown as well as in compiling the catalogue notes and identifying binders of unsigned examples. Their specialized knowledge and cooperation have been invaluable. I am grateful for their help and interest shown in the exhibition.

I am indebted to my associates Alexandra Dodd Schultze, who assisted in details of the catalogue, and John S. Van E. Kohn, who made possible the acquisition of some bindings in the collection and who also generously presented me with fine examples. I owe much too to my many colleagues and friends in the world of antiquarian books for calling my attention to and for gifts of American bindings. Fine examples have found their way back to this country from England and France and one choice binding was found in Denmark.

My profound gratitude goes to the Directors and Curators of the participating institutions for their cooperation in sponsoring the tour and attending to the many details of organizing and circulating the exhibition, and for valuable suggestions in printing and publication of the catalogue. My admiration and warm thanks to the officers and staffs of The Meriden Gravure Company and The Stinehour Press, who, working under difficult conditions and pressure of time, somehow managed to produce the catalogue.

Above all, the collection owes more than I can say to the encouragement and enthusiasm of my late wife and companion of thirty-eight years, Eleanor Clermont Papantonio, who was with us at the January meeting, and who frequently produced a surprise binding on birthdays, Christmas, or anniversaries.

M. P.

Yonkers, New York
August, 1972

INTRODUCTION

THIS exhibition of American bindings from the collection of Michael Papantonio has been long and eagerly awaited. It has been sixty-five years since the bindings collected by Beverly Chew were exhibited at the Grolier Club, whose membership lists include the names of both collectors. Unfortunately the Grolier Club catalogue was not illustrated. Since that date, 1907, I know of only one exhibition devoted exclusively to American bindings, that of the work of the distinguished binder of eighteenth-century Philadelphia, Robert Aitken, arranged by Carol and Willman Spawn at the Free Library of Philadelphia in December, 1960.

Michael Papantonio has been favored in his collecting by his position as dealer in antiquarian books, with ready access to the marketplace. Not content with mere acquisition, he has generously shared his collection with students and admirers of American binding and has contributed both directly and indirectly to an enlarged knowledge of this once obscure bypath of binding history. To those of us who have travelled far in search of examples of the American binder's work this sampling from a much larger collection made over the last twenty-five years is of great importance and satisfaction both for its extent and for its quality.

The books shown here cover a span of two centuries, ranging from the work of John Ratcliffe in Boston in 1669 to that of Pawson and Nicholson in Philadelphia in 1864. Not all bindings date within the year of printing. In fact, three shown here were executed long years after the books were printed, though a majority were bound within the year of printing or a few years thereafter. The exhibition traces the shift in importance as a center for the craft from Boston to Philadelphia in the eighteenth century, and to New York in the nineteenth century. It also includes work by craftsmen in lesser places: Salem, Massachusetts; Newport and Providence, Rhode Island; New Haven and Hartford, Connecticut; Germantown, Pennsylvania; Georgetown, District of Columbia; Annapolis, Maryland—leaving only the southern colonies of Virginia and South Carolina unrepresented.

A dozen bindings in the exhibition are signed by ticket or tooling, introducing a number of binders who might not be known otherwise. The work of many more craftsmen than those appearing in the Grolier Club exhibition has been confidently identified from long and close studies of tools. The career of Francis Skinner of Newport covers fifty years or better, from about 1730 to 1785. Caleb Buglass and James Muir were at work in Philadelphia at the height of that city's reputation as a binding center. In Boston Henry Bilson Legge and John Roulstone were turning out fine bindings after the trade became centered in New York. The Papantonio collection proudly presents a panorama of American bindings from widely scattered locations, with new work and new names.

HANNAH DUSTIN FRENCH

CATALOGUE

❧ JOHN RATCLIFF or RATCLIFFE, Boston

1. Nathaniel Morton. New-Englands Memoriall. Cambridge [Mass.]: S[amuel]. G[reen]. and M[armaduke]. J[ohnson]. for John Usher of Boston, 1669.

Quarto, 6¾ x 5½ inches, russet sheep, gilt, "Thomas Deane" stamped in gilt within gilt border in center panels of both covers, sprinkled edges, remains of two clasps.

Bound by John Ratcliffe, brought over from London to bind the Eliot Indian Bible in 1663. A copy of the Indian Bible at Bowdoin College bears the same tools.

PROVENANCE. Inscribed, "Thomas Deane. Abigail White, March the 29th 1700." Shipdham Church Library, sale Hodgson March 29, 1950, Lot 129. Bookplate of H. R. Creswick, Librarian of Cambridge University. Sotheby Sale, June 11, 1963, Lot 142, with illustration.

REFERENCES. Thomas Deane, see Sibley, *Biographical Sketches of Graduates of Harvard University* (1881), II, 208. Bernard Bailyn, *New England Merchants in the Seventeenth Century* (1955), pp. 122–123. John Ratcliffe, see Hannah D. French, *Bookbinding in America* (1941), pp. 11, 16. Thomas J. Holmes, in the initial study of Ratcliffe, American Antiquarian Society, *Proceedings*, n.s., XXXVIII (April, 1928), 31–50, omitted Eliot's Indian Bible.

❧ JOHN RATCLIFF or RATCLIFFE, Boston

2. Boston. Synod, 1680. A Confession of Faith. Boston: John Foster, 1680.

Octavo, 5¾ x 3¾ inches, brown sheep, blind-tooled, sprinkled edges.

Bound by John Ratcliffe. Ratcliffe received nine pounds, one cord of wood, and eleven shillings from the Colony of Massachusetts Bay for the edition binding of this book. S. A. Green, *John Foster* (1909), pp. 110–111.

PROVENANCE. Inscribed, "Tho Wallcut, Bo[s], 1 Aug[t] 1793." Stamp of American Antiquarian Society. Armorial bookplate of Alfred Bates, laid in.

REFERENCES. William G. Land, "Further Notes on Ratcliff and Ranger Bindings," American Antiquarian Society, *Proceedings*, n.s., XXXIX (October, 1929), 304.

ANDREW BRADFORD's shop, Philadelphia

3. The Laws of Pennsylvania. Philadelphia: Andrew Bradford, 1728.

Folio, 11⅞ x 7⅞ inches, sheep, blind-tooled boards and board edges, sprinkled edges.

Binding ascribed to Andrew Bradford's shop. Bradford printed two editions of the collected laws, of which this is the second. He came to Philadelphia in 1712 and set up as a stationer at the "Sign of the Bible"; in 1717 he leased the printing press and type belonging to the Society of Friends (Quakers), which he operated until his death in 1742.

PROVENANCE. Inscribed, "James Hunter's [Philadelphia] 1760."

SOMBER MOROCCO BINDING, Boston

4. Thomas Prince. Christ Abolishing Death. . . . Boston: Printed by J. Draper, for D. Henchman, 1736.

Mather Byles. To His Excellency Governor Belcher on the Death of his Lady. An Epistle. [Boston, 1736.]

Two volumes in one. Quarto, 9 x 7 inches. Black morocco, blind-tooled. Five raised cords on back, board edges and turn-ins blind-tooled, comb-marbled endpapers, edges stained black. Thick paper copies.

PROVENANCE: Inscribed, "J. Belcher"; "Mary Emelia Elizabeth Jennison, presented to her by her Honored Father in the year 1775" (her mother's funeral sermon and elegy). Bookplate of Jonathan Belcher.

MOROCCO BINDING, Boston

5. The Psalms, Hymns, and Spiritual Songs. Boston: S. Kneeland & T. Green, 1737.

12mo, 5 x 3 inches, black morocco, comb-marbled endpapers, edges gilt.

PROVENANCE. Inscribed, "Frances Gardner, Leominster."

FRANCIS SKINNER, Newport

6. Jeremiah Burroughs. Two Treatises. . . . London: Peter Cole, 1649. Bound ca. 1750.

Quarto, 7⅜ x 5½ inches, mid-18th-century sheep, plain flat spine, repaired, blind stamped, with the name of the city, Newport, stamped vertically within a scroll design, on both covers. A most unusual decoration for American bindings of the period. Similar designs are found on 18th-century pocketbooks.

Bound by Francis Skinner, Newport, with his signature, "Fra: Skinners," on the first page of text.

PROVENANCE. James Cahoone. Francis Skinner. Susannah W. Thorne, 1820.

REFERENCES. Carol M. and Willman Spawn, "Francis Skinner, Bookbinder of Newport . . . ," *Winterthur Portfolio*, II (1965), 47–61. William A. Jackson, "Our Ingenious Ancestors," reprinted from the 1963 Walpole Society *Note Book*; Skinner's label (or advertisement) reproduced, facing p. 4.

❧ CALF BINDING, New York

7. Petrus Sacharie Nakskow. The Articles of Faith of the Holy Evangelical Church. . . . New York: Printed and sold, J. Parker and W. Weyman, Also to be sold by Godfried Muller . . . in New York, and Mr. Schleydorn in Phila., 1754.

Quarto, 9 x 6¾ inches, tan calf, gilt board edges, comb-marbled endpapers, gilt edges.

PROVENANCE. E. A. Brinckerhoff.

❧ MOROCCO BINDING, Boston

8. The Psalms, Hymns, and Spiritual Songs. Boston: D. Henchman & S. Kneeland, 1758.

Octavo, 6¼ x 4 inches, red morocco, gilt board edges and page edges.

PROVENANCE. Inscribed, "Charles Deane, Cambridge." Deane Sale, March 30, 1898. James Frothingham Hunnewell (bookplate).

Psalm books were the exception to the usual blind-tooled bindings of New England and were gilt from the 17th century onwards. The Kalbfleish copy of the third edition of the *Bay Psalm Book* (1651), now in the New York Public Library, is illustrated in W. L. Andrews' *Bibliopegy in the United States* (1902), p. 32.

❧ CHRISTOPHER HOFFMANN, Philadelphia County

9. Schwenkfelders. Neue Eingerichtetes Gesang-Buch. Germantown: Christopher Saur, 1762.

Octavo, 7½ x 5⅜ inches, calf over bevelled wooden boards, clasps from rear board, edges stained red.

Binding ascribed to Christopher Hoffmann, Schwenkfelder minister and binder, who bound various editions for his church; see Caspar Schwenkfelder's *Erlauterung* (Breslau and Leipzig, 1771), documented by receipts in the Schwenkfelder Library at Pennsburg, Pa., as well as Evans Nos. 9512, 9266, 18779, and 23975. Hoffmann's tools were unlike those of his German contemporaries, in fact are strongly reminiscent of some used on Irish bindings, suggesting that he acquired a lot of second-hand tools from an Irish source.

PROVENANCE. Swann Sale, March 31, 1966.

❧ ANDREW BARCLAY, Boston

9A. Bible. O. T. Psalms.

N. Brady and N. Tate. A New Version of the Psalms of David. Boston: W. McAlpine & J. Fleeming, 1765.

A Collection of Hymns from Dr. Watts &c. Boston: W. M'Alpine & J. Fleeming, 1765.

Daniel Bayley. The Psalm-Singer's Assistant. Newbury-Port: Printed for and Sold by the Author, [1767].

Three volumes in one. 12mo, 6¼ x 3½ inches. Brown morocco, gilt edges, marbled endpapers, by Andrew Barclay, with his engraved bookbinder's label.

PROVENANCE: Inscribed, "M. Davis, 1824"; "Mr. Parrott." Thomas W. Streeter, October 21, 1969, lot 4167.

REFERENCES: Hannah D. French, "The Amazing Career of Andrew Barclay, Scottish Bookbinder, of Boston," *Studies in Bibliography. Papers of the Bibliographical Society of the University of Virginia*, XIV (1961), 150.

❧ ANDREW BARCLAY, Boston

10. [Laurence Sterne.] A Sentimental Journey. 2 vols. [Boston: Mein & Fleming], 1768.

12mo, 6¼ x 3½ inches, red morocco, gilt board edges, sprinkled edges.

Ascribed to Andrew Barclay, binder.

PROVENANCE. Inscribed, "Eliza A. Whittemore."

REFERENCES. Hannah D. French, "The Amazing Career of Andrew Barclay, Scottish Bookbinder of Boston," *Studies in Bibliography. Papers of the Bibliographical Society of the University of Virginia*, XIV (1961), 145–162.

❧ WILLIAM AIKMAN, Annapolis

11. Elie Vallette. The Deputy Commissary's Guide. Annapolis: Anne Catharine Green and Son, 1774.

Octavo, 8 x 5¼ inches, calf, red morocco title label, gilt board edges, marbled endpapers.

Binding ascribed to William Aikman, Annapolis. In 1773–75 Aikman had extensive accounts with Robert Aitken of Philadelphia. After his removal to Jamaica about 1775, his distinctive tool, the undulating three-line fillet above and below the label here, appears on Jamaican imprints from the late 1770s into the 1780s.

PROVENANCE. Inscribed, "The Gift of Elie Vallette to his Friend John McNabb."

❧ ROBERT AITKEN's shop, Philadelphia

12. John Gregory. A Father's Legacy to His Daughters. London, Printed: Philadelphia: Re-printed by John Dunlap, 1775.

Small octavo, 6¼ x 4⅛ inches, calf with red morocco title label, gilt board edges and turn-ins, comb-marbled endpapers, stained edges.

Bound in Robert Aitken's shop, Philadelphia. The same combination of tools appears on a copy of Steuben's *Regulations* (at the Boston Athenæum) bound by Aitken for presentation to George Washington, as recorded in the Aitken Waste Book at the Library Company of Philadelphia. The decorative roll appears on a copy of the Aitken Bible presented to Aitken's friend Ebenezer Hazard (at British Museum).

PROVENANCE. Inscribed, "For Miss A. Redman."

REFERENCES. Willman and Carol Spawn, "R. Aitken, Colonial Printer of Philadelphia," *Graphic Arts Review* (Philadelphia), January–February, 1961.

❧ ROBERT AITKEN's shop, Philadelphia

13. Hugh Blair. Lectures on Rhetoric and Belles Lettres. Philadelphia: Robert Aitken, 1784. Thick paper copy.

Quarto, 10⅝ x 8⅝ inches, red morocco with green morocco title label, gilt board edges and turn-ins, marbled endpapers, stained and polished edges.

Bound in Robert Aitken's shop, Philadelphia. Five copies of Blair's *Lectures* in this binding (all with variant spines) are known, three in red morocco and two in marbled calf. One morocco copy and one calf copy are on thin paper.

PROVENANCE. Inscribed, "Jas. W. Dale. Bought at sale of Books belonging to Hon. Charles Thompson Secretary of Congress. Sale at Newark Dela."

REFERENCES. Willman and Carol Spawn, "The Aitken Shop: Identification of an Eighteenth-century Bindery and Its Tools," *Papers of the Bibliographical Society of America*, LVII (1963), 422–437. Walters Art Gallery, Baltimore, *The History of Bookbinding, 525-1950 A.D.* (Baltimore, 1957), no. 605, p. 240.

❧ CALEB BUGLASS, Philadelphia

14. John Parke. The Lyric Works of Horace Translated into English Verse. Philadelphia: Eleazer Oswald, 1786.

Octavo, 8 x 5 inches, red morocco with black morocco title label added later, gilt board edges and turn-ins, gilt edges.

Bound by Caleb Buglass, Philadelphia.

PROVENANCE. One of the dedication copies with inscription, "The Honorable Robert Morris Esq. Member of the General Assembly of the Commonwealth from his very humble Servt the Author. Philadelphia February 10, 1787." Edward D. Ingraham (bookplate).

REFERENCES. Hannah D. French, "Caleb Buglass, Binder of the Proposed Book of Common Prayer, Philadelphia 1786," *Winterthur Portfolio*, 6, 15–32.

❧ CALEB BUGLASS, Philadelphia

15. Protestant Episcopal Church. The Book of Common Prayer. Philadelphia: Hall and Sellers, 1786.

Small octavo, 6½ x 4⅛ inches, red morocco, gilt board edges, comb-marbled endpapers, gilt edges.

Bound by Caleb Buglass, Philadelphia.

PROVENANCE. D. F. Appleton (bookplate). Beverly Chew (bookplate). A. Edward Newton. Otis T. Bradley, New York.

REFERENCES. Hannah D. French, "Caleb Buglass, Binder of the Proposed Book of Common Prayer, Philadelphia 1786," *Winterthur Portfolio*, 6, 15–32.

❧ FRANKLIN'S HEAD shop, New York

16. The Federalist. A Collection of Essays written in favour of the New Constitution, as agreed upon by The Federal Convention, September 17, 1787. 2 vols. New-York: Printed and sold by J. and A. M'Lean, No. 41 Hanover-Square, 1788.

12mo, 6⅝ x 4¼ inches, brown mottled calf, green and red morocco labels in the second and fourth panels, green morocco volume number onlays within gilt wreaths on the red labels, fillets on edges of covers, gilt dentelle turn-ins, marbled endpapers, edges sprinkled in light red.

Binding ascribed to J. and A. M'Lean. Printed slip tipped into the front of each volume: "Printed and Bound, at Franklin's Head, No. 41, Hanover-Square."

Printed on thick paper, bound with a number of blank leaves at the end of volume I, so as to have the volumes of uniform thickness. A small number of copies were issued on thick paper and presumably all bound by the M'Leans, some more elaborately tooled than others. There are variations in the tooling, but all copies seen have the same Greek key pattern on the edges of the covers and the onlays for the volume numbers.

The identical center ornament in the compartments on spines was used on the Lennox copy (N.Y.P.L.), reproduced by Poor, p. 77. The gilt turn-ins decorated with the same roll as that used on the George Washington–W. W. Hearst (now Henry Bradley Martin, New York) copy, presented to Washington by Alexander Hamilton and delivered by James Madison (reproduced in The Grolier Club Catalogue of *One Hundred Influential American Books* [New York, 1947], p. 57). Another thick paper copy was sold in the E. H. Litchfield sale, Parke-Bernet Galleries, December 3, 1951, Lot 375 (binding reproduced). French, p. 119, noting the copy in the New York Public Library.

PROVENANCE: Inscribed "Joseph Dixon, Whitehaven, Purchased at New York October 1st, 1789," on titles of both volumes; and on the blank leaf at the end of Volume II, in the same hand is the notation: "The foregoing papers are supposed to be written by Mr. Maddison [sic] – Hamilton – Jay & Livingston." William R. Weeks, New York, sold at Henkels, Philadelphia, March 5, 1902, Lot 435.

❧ JAMES MUIR, Philadelphia

17. Charles Churchill. Poems. 2 vols. [New York: James Rivington], 1768. Bound ca. 1790.

Octavo, 8⅜ x 5½ inches, tree calf with red morocco title label and green morocco onlays for volume numbers, gilt board edges, marbled endpapers, polished green edges.

Binding ascribed to James Muir, Philadelphia. See the references for the Collins Bible, 1791.

❧ JAMES MUIR, Philadelphia

18. Protestant Episcopal Church. The Book of Common Prayer. Philadelphia: Hall and Sellers, 1790.

12mo, 6⅞ x 4½ inches, red morocco, gilt board edges, comb-marbled endpapers, gilt edges.

Bound by James Muir, Philadelphia.

PROVENANCE. Inscribed, "From my old & respected Friend Mrs Eliz^{h} Pinckney Wid^{o} of Charles Pinckney Esq. Chief Justice of the province of South Carolina." George Keate, Esq. Brook Kay, 1852. Sotheby, June 1, 1943, Lot 107. Major J. R. Abbey. Sotheby, June 19, 1967, Lot 1794.

REFERENCES. Michael Papantonio, "A Note on the Binding of Smith's Wealth of Nations," *Princeton University Library Chronicle*, XXXII, no. 2 (Winter, 1971).

❧ MOROCCO BINDING, Boston

19. Jeremy Belknap. The History of New-Hampshire. Boston: Thomas and Andrews, 1791. Volume II only.

Octavo, 8¼ x 5 inches, green morocco, four onlays on spine, title and volume labels and head and foot of spine, in red, gilt board edges and turn-ins, marbled endpapers, polished edges.

Evidently bound to match the green morocco Volume I done by Robert Aitken. Tools are similar but not the same as those owned by Aitken.

PROVENANCE. Discarded from Tenney Memorial Library, Newbury, Vt. (bookplate).

REFERENCES. The first volume of Belknap's *History* had been printed in Philadelphia in 1784 by Robert Aitken. Aitken's Waste Book contains an account with Belknap, under date of August 10, 1784 (p. 401), for binding two copies of the first volume in "Extra toold Green Morocco, broad Gold border," at eighteen shillings each. Willman and Carol Spawn, "The Aitken Shop," *Papers of the Bibliographical Society of America*, LVII, 422–437.

❧ HENRY BILSON LEGGE, Boston

20. The Holy Bible. Worcester: Isaiah Thomas, 1791.

Bound in two volumes, quarto, 11½ x 9¼ inches, red roan, gilt board edges, marbled endpapers, sprinkled edges.

Binding ascribed to Henry Bilson Legge.

PROVENANCE. Family record of William Dinsmore and Katherine Brown Dinsmore, Windham, N.H., 1803.

REFERENCES. Hannah D. French, "Bound in Boston by Henry B. Legg," *Studies in Bibliography. Papers of the Bibliographical Society of the University of Virginia*, XVII (1964), 135–139.

❧ JAMES MUIR, Philadelphia

21. The Holy Bible. Trenton: Isaac Collins, 1791.

Quarto, 10½ x 8⅜ inches, tree calf with red morocco title label, gilt board edges, marbled endpapers, gilt edges.

Bound by James Muir, Philadelphia. Muir worked for Robert Aitken in 1775, and their continuing association is illustrated by Muir's use of an Aitken tool here. The scroll in the spine panel of the Bible is identical to that in the lower corners of the board of the Aitken Blair (1784).

PROVENANCE. Inscribed "The within sheets were presented to James Ewing as an acknowledgment for his attention in correcting the Press. Trenton, August 1st, 1792. By the Printer." Carroll Atwood Wilson (bookplate).

REFERENCES. M. Papantonio, "A Note on the Binding of Smith's Wealth of Nations," *Princeton University Library Chronicle*, XXXII, no. 2 (Winter, 1971).

❧ CHARLES CLELAND, New York

22. The Self-Interpreting Bible. . . . By the late Reverend John Brown. Engraved illustrations. New York: Hodge and Campbell, 1792.

Folio, 16¾ x 10½ inches, red morocco, rebacked; original spine laid down, gilt board edges, marbled endpapers, gilt edges.

Binding ascribed to Charles Cleland.

PROVENANCE. Charles E. Goodspeed (bookplate).

The first complete edition of the Bible printed in New York. The binding of another copy with the name "Mary Ellis 1792," bound by Thomas Allen, is reproduced as the frontispiece in Poor, and described in Grolier. Washington's copy, whose name heads the list of subscribers, bound in red morocco, is in the library of The Masonic Lodge, Alexandria, Va. The volume was first issued in parts.

HENRY BILSON LEGGE, Boston

23. George Washington. Official Letters to the Honourable American Congress. 2 vols., Boston: Manning & Loring, 1795.

12mo, 7¼ x 4¼ inches, tree calf, gilt board edges, marbled endpapers.

Bound by Henry Bilson Legge.

PROVENANCE. Inscribed, "N. s. Gilman."

CALF BINDING, New York

24. Paul Wright. The New and Complete Life of . . . Jesus Christ. New York: Birdsall and Menut, 1795.

Folio, 13 x 8 inches, mottled calf, red morocco labels for title and owner's name, G. Furman, gilt board edges, blue marbled endpapers, sprinkled edges.

PROVENANCE. Inscribed, "This Book was presented to A[bigail] S[picer] Irving (wife of John Treat Irving) by her Father Gabriel Furman on Tuesday Decr the 6th 1831."

HENRY BILSON LEGGE, Boston

25. George Washington. Washington's Political Legacies. Boston: Printed for John Russell and John West, 1800.

Octavo, 8 x 4¾ inches, dark blue morocco, red morocco title label, eight red overlays dividing the spine, gilt board edges and turn-ins, marbled endpapers, gilt edges.

Bound by Henry Bilson Legge.

REFERENCES. Compare Boston Public Library copy reproduced in Hannah D. French, *Bookbinding in America* (1941), Fig. 24, opposite p. 74.

❧ PETER A. MESIER, New York

26. Protestant Episcopal Church. The Book of Common Prayer. New York: Peter A. Mesier, 1806.

Octavo, 9½ x 5¾ inches, contemporary red straight-grained morocco, gilt corners on board edges, gilt turn-ins, marbled endpapers, gauffered gilt edges.

Binding ascribed to Peter A. Mesier. A copy of the *Book of Common Prayer* printed by Hugh Gaine in 1793 at the William L. Clements Library carries Mesier's label as binder.

PROVENANCE. "Mrs. J. G. Glonney" vertically in gilt on front cover.

❧ ROBERT DE SILVER, Philadelphia

27. Joel Barlow. The Columbiad. Philadelphia: Fry & Kammerer, 1807.

Quarto, 11½ x 9¼ inches, calf, blind-tooled with marbled center panel, black morocco title label, board edges gilt at corners, gilt turn-ins, colored endpapers, sprinkled edges.

Bound by Robert De Silver, with his ticket.

PROVENANCE. Rev. J. Cohen. Walter R. Steiner.

REFERENCES. For additional bindings by De Silver see Walters Art Gallery, Baltimore, *The History of Bookbinding, 525–1950 A.D.* (Baltimore, 1957), Nos. 612, 613, pp. 242–243. The Grolier Club, New York, *Catalogue of Ornamental Bookbindings . . .* (New York, 1907), Nos. 56, 57, pp. 46–47.

❧ S. WADSWORTH, New Haven

28. David Ramsay. The Life of George Washington. New York: Hopkins & Seymour, 1807.

Octavo, 9 x 5¼ inches, tree calf, title label, gilt board edges, marbled endpapers, sprinkled edges.

Bound by S. Wadsworth, New Haven, with his ticket.

PROVENANCE. Inscribed, "William Hart. Lucy Hart. Mrs. Lucy Smith."

☙ JOHN ROULSTONE, Boston

29. Isaiah Thomas. The History of Printing in America. 2 vols. Worcester: Isaiah Thomas, Jun., 1810.

Octavo, 8¾ x 5¼ inches, diced russia, gilt board edges and turn-ins, marbled endpapers, polished edges.

Bound by John Roulstone of Boston.

PROVENANCE. E. Harold Hugo (bookplate and printed label).

REFERENCES. Hannah D. French, *Bookbinding in America* (1941), p. 72. Hannah D. French, "John Roulstone's Harvard Bindings," *Harvard Library Bulletin*, XVIII, no. 2 (April, 1970), 171–182.

☙ JOHN ROULSTONE, Boston

30. Liturgy Collected for the Use of the Church at King's Chapel. Second Edition. Boston: Joshua Belcher, 1811.

Octavo, 8¾ x 5½ inches, red, straight-grained morocco, gilt board edges and turn-ins, marbled endpapers, gilt edges.

Bound by John Roulstone.

Another copy, at Winterthur, has the name of T. Heard, Jun., tooled inside the elipse on the center cover and has triangular cornerpieces on its covers; otherwise the same tooling.

☙ T. PRINCE, Salem

31. Protestant Episcopal Church. The Book of Common Prayer. Boston: Published by Charles Williams, J. T. Buckingham, Printer, 1811.

Octavo, 9 x 5¼ inches, red morocco, gilt board edges and turn-ins, colored endpapers, gauffered gilt edges.

Bound by T. Prince, Salem, with his ticket.

PROVENANCE. "Catherine W. Codman" tooled lengthwise of front cover. Bookseller's label (formerly pasted over binder's label): "Sold by R. P. & C. Williams, Wholesale and Retail Booksellers, Cornhill Square, Boston."

REFERENCES. Harriet S. Tapley, *Salem Imprints, 1768–1825* (1927), p. 205.

❧ JOHN ROULSTONE, Boston

32. John Locke. An Essay Concerning Human Understanding. 2 vols. Boston: Cummings & Hilliard and J. T. Buckingham, 1813.

Octavo, 8½ x 5¼ inches, Spanish calf, red title and volume labels, gilt board edges, marbled endpapers, polished edges.

Bound by John Roulstone.

PROVENANCE. Inscribed, "E. J. Hoyt's 1814. A. W. Hoyt, 1850, Deerfield, Mass."

❧ JOHN ROULSTONE, Boston

33. Maria Edgeworth. The Parent's Assistant. 3 vols. Boston: W. Wells and T. B. Wait, 1814.

12mo, 5⅞ x 3⅝ inches, Spanish mottled calf, red morocco title and volume labels, gilt board edges, colored endpapers, sprinkled edges.

Binding ascribed to John Roulstone.

PROVENANCE. Inscribed, "William B. Carter." Pencilled note of M. Papantonio, "Elizabeth Gunn, Boston, collector of juvenile literature. Probably by Roulstone, cf. Eustaphieve which follows."

❧ J. KATEZ, Philadelphia

34. Elias Boudinot. The Second Advent. Trenton: D. Fenton and S. Hutchinson, 1815.

Octavo, 8⅛ x 5⅜ inches, red straight-grained morocco, gilt- and blind-tooled, gilt board edges and turn-ins, green endpapers with leather hinges.

Bound by J. Katez, Philadelphia, with his ticket.

PROVENANCE. Stamped, "Mrs. Julia Rush" in gilt at bottom of spine. Carroll Atwood Wilson (bookplate). R. Esmerian, Parke-Bernet, October 13, 1970, Lot 34.

☙ JOHN ROULSTONE, Boston

35. Alexis Eustaphieve. Demetrius, the Hero of the Don. Boston: Munroe & Francis, 1818.

12mo, 7 x 4½ inches, scarlet roan, board edges and turn-ins gilt, marbled endpapers, edges gilt.

Bound by John Roulstone.

PROVENANCE. The dedication copy to the Empress Elizabeth of Russia. Stamp of Bibliotheque de Tsarskoe Selo (sale New York, 1934). The author was Consul General of Russia at Boston. R. Esmerian, Parke-Bernet, October 13, 1970, Lot 35.

☙ WM. W. POTTER, Philadelphia

36. Sir Walter Scott. Works. 6 vols. New York: J. Eastburn and Co., 1818.

12mo, 5½ x 3⅜ inches, mottled calf, gilt- and blind-tooled with black and green morocco title labels, gilt board edges and turn-ins.

Bound by Wm. W. Potter, Philadelphia, with his ticket.

☙ JOHN ROULSTONE, Boston

37. [Washington Irving.] The Sketch Book. Parts I–V. New-York: C. S. Van Winkle, 1819.

Octavo, 8½ x 5¼ inches, scarlet straight-grained morocco, gilt- and blind-tooled, gilt board edges and turn-ins, marbled endpapers, gilt edges.

Bound by John Roulstone.

PROVENANCE. Inscribed, "Presented to Horatio Robinson, from his friend, Norris Marshall Jones, May 12th 1820." Printed book label of Norris Marshall Jones. Gilt red leather bookplate of Richard Montgomery Gilchrist Potter.

☙ MILLER & HUTCHENS, Providence

38. [Washington Irving.] The Sketch Book. Parts I–VII. 2 vols., New-York: C. S. Van Winkle, 1819.

Octavo, 8½ x 5 inches, russia, gilt- and blind-tooled, gilt board edges, blind-tooled turn-ins, marbled endpapers, sprinkled edges.

Binder's ticket reading, "Re-bound by Miller & Hutchens."

John Miller and John Hutchens were printers, publishers, bookbinders, and booksellers in Providence from 1815 to 1823. Miller attended to the printing and publishing; Hutchens to the bookbinding and bookselling, according to the Brown's *Directory of Printing, Publishing, Bookselling and Allied Trades in Rhode Island to 1865* (1960).

☙ Ascribed to HENRY I. MEGAREY, New York

39. Protestant Episcopal Church. The Book of Common Prayer. New York: Henry I. Megarey, 1819.

Octavo, 8¾ x 5⅝ inches, red morocco, gilt- and blind-tooled, gilt board edges and turn-ins, colored endpapers, gilt edges.

Binding ascribed to Henry I. Megarey. Megarey bound a number of copies of his publication. Three copies, with slight variations in the tooling, were exhibited at the Grolier Club; one, with the name "Beverly Chew" on the cover, has Megarey's ticket; another belonged to William Loring Andrews, who described and illustrated the binding in his *Biblopegy*. Andrews quotes Richard Grant White's high praise of the binding on another copy of the volume. White was unaware of the binder's name.

PROVENANCE. Pencilled contemporary (?) name "C. Cecelia Rogers[?]" on recto of frontispiece.

REFERENCES. Andrews, pp. 14–15. Grolier 40–42.

☙ T. H. BURNTON, Providence

40. James W. Eastburn. Yamoyden. New-York: James Eastburn, 1820.

12mo, 7¼ x 4¼ inches, Spanish calf, gilt- and blind-tooled, gilt corners and center of board edges, gilt turn-ins, colored endpapers, sprinkled edges.

Bound by T. H. Burnton, Providence, R.I., with his ticket.

PROVENANCE. Inscribed, "Eleanor Burrill, from Wm. R. W. Green," in pencil. "Miss Eleanor Burrill, from her friend, W. R. G.," in ink.

According to the directories Thomas H. Burnton was a bookbinder in New York from 1800 to 1806, and in Providence from 1821 to 1828.

☙ GEORGE CHAMPLEY, New York

41. James Beattie. The Minstrel . . . and Other Poems. New York: R. & W. A. Bartow . . . , 1821.

12mo, 5⅝ x 3⅝ inches, citron straight-grained morocco, gilt- and blind-tooled, oval prize stamp of Mrs. O'Kill's school in gilt on front covers, gilt board edges, marbled endpapers, marbled edges.

Bound by George Champley, New York.

Prize volume awarded to Miss Julia Low, a pupil attending Mrs. Mary O'Kill's school in New York. The name of the engraver of the large oval in the center of the front cover, J. D. Stout, is in the lower right-hand side. Three additional examples of O'Kill prize volumes, with Champley's tickets, are in the collection. Another is reproduced in Poor, pp. 46–49, noted and described in the Grolier, No. 39.

☙ JOHN MARCH, Georgetown

42. John B. Colvin. Historical Letters, Including a Brief but General View of the History of the World. Second edition. Georgetown, D.C.: Joseph Milligan, 1821.

12mo, 6¾ x 4¼ inches, red roan with gilt board edges, marbled endpapers, sprinkled edges.

Bound by John March, Georgetown. Thomas Jefferson was one of March's customers, according to M. Sowerby's *Catalogue of the Library of Thomas Jefferson* (Washington, 1952).

☙ CALF BINDING, Worcester

43. Aaron Bancroft. Sermons. Worcester [Mass.]: William Manning & Son, 1822.

Octavo, 8½ x 5¼ inches, calf, gilt- and blind-tooled with light center panel having black lines, spine stained black, green morocco title label, gilt board edges, colored endpapers with red leather hinge, sprinkled edges.

PROVENANCE. Inscribed, "Lucretia Bancroft, From her Father, 1837."

❧ MOROCCO BINDING, Philadelphia

44. Washington Irving. Tales of a Traveler. Two parts in one volume. Philadelphia: H. C. Carey and I. Lea, 1824.

Octavo, 8¼ x 5¾ inches, red morocco, gilt board edges and turn-ins, lavender silk doublures with leather hinges, gauffered gilt edges with initials "S. E. K."

PROVENANCE. Inscribed, "Presented to S. E. Knight by her friend G. A. Shryock Sept. 1824."

❧ GEORGE CHAMPLEY, New York

45. The Album. New-York: F & R Lockwood, 1824.

12mo, 7⅛ x 4⅜ inches, red straight-grained morocco, gilt- and blind-stamped, gilt board edges and turn-ins, waxed colored endpapers, gilt edges.

Binding ascribed to G. Champley, New York.

Copies exist on large paper, measuring about 1¼ inches taller. A copy in the collection has an engraved title with the imprint of G. Champley, New York, replacing the engraved title used by Lockwood. The text imposed in fours.

The Grolier exhibition catalogue (Nos. 37 and 38) describes two copies, both presumably large paper copies, both in red straight-grained morocco, with G. Champley's ticket.

PROVENANCE. Miss Ann S. Dwight, November, 1824.

❧ MOROCCO BINDING, Philadelphia

46. William Shakespeare. The Dramatic Works. 2 vols. Philadelphia: M'Carty & Davis, H. C. Carey & I. Lea, 1824.

Octavo, 8⅜ x 5¾ inches, blue straight-grained morocco gilt- and blind-tooled, gilt board edges and turn-ins, purple silk doublures with leather hinges, gilt edges.

❧ WILSON & NICHOLS, New York

47. Cadwallader David Colden. Memoir . . . at the Celebration of the Completion of the New York Canals. New York: W. A. Davis, 1825.

Quarto, 10 x 8 inches, red straight-grained morocco, gilt presentation stamp on front cover: "PRESENTED BY THE CITY OF NEW YORK TO [seal of the City of New York in blind] THOMAS BALDOCK ESQR. COMMANDER OF H.B.M. SLOOP OF WAR SWALLOW." Gilt board edges and turn-ins, colored waxed endpapers, gilt edges.

Name of binder, "WILSON & NICHOLS BIND.," at foot of spine.

Commander Baldock's sloop was in New York harbor at the time of the celebration, and is mentioned on pp. 351–352 of the volume. Following the preface is a leaf headed: "Directions to Messrs Wilson and Nicholls [sic], Bookbinders, No. 2, Pine Street. For placing the [47] plates." Wilson and Nichols bound a number of copies of this handsome work for presentation to prominent people, mainly New Yorkers. One was presented to Lafayette. Andrews (p. 98) reproduces the front cover and spine of the copy presented to Robert Lennox. Other copies in the Papantonio collection are presented to David T. Valentine (red morocco) and Hon. John T. Irving (brown calf). There is some variation in the tooling.

One hundred forty-four bookbinders formed the twenty-fourth body in the line of march, preceded by the printers and followed by the booksellers, stationers, and music dealers. Some binders are named. A huge volume in red morocco, measuring four feet eight inches by three feet, labelled "Erie Canal Statistics," finished by John Bradford and Isaac Peckham, was mounted on a handbarrow. For a more detailed account of this sumptuous publication see the Grolier, Nos. 46 and 47, the latter presented to Theodorus Bailey, Post Master.

☙ MOROCCO BINDING, Boston

48. Felicia Hemans. The League of the Alps. 2 vols., Boston: Hilliard, Gray, Little, and Wilkins, 1826.

Octavo, 8½ x 5½ inches, scarlet straight-grained morocco, gilt- and blind-tooled, title and volume labels, gilt board edges and turn-ins, marbled endpapers, gilt edges.

PREVENANCE. George A. Zabriskie (bookplate).

☙ CALF BINDING, New York

49. Samuel B. H. Judah. The Buccaneers; A Romance of our own Country in its Antient day. . . . Second edition. 2 vols. Boston: Munroe & Francis, 1827.

12mo, 7¼ x 4½ inches, tan calf, gilt- and blind-tooled, gilt board edges and turn-ins, gilt edges. A family copy, in a special binding.

Three additional titles by Judah are in the collection, all similarly bound. Two others, *The Mountain Torrent* (1820) and *A Tale of Lexington* (1823), bound in one volume, are in the C. Waller Barrett collection at the University of Virginia library.

PROVENANCE. Miss Hildegarde Whitehead, New York City and Westport, N.Y., a descendant of the author. Acquired from Miss Whitehead August, 1957.

CATHEDRAL PANEL BINDING

50. Nathaniel P. Willis. Sketches. Boston: S. G. Goodrich, 1827.

Octavo, 8½ x 5 inches, black morocco cathedral binding, gilt- and blind-tooled, gilt board edges and turn-ins, marbled endpapers, sprinkled edges.

PROVENANCE. Inscribed, "To S. B. Van Schaick, Esq., with the most sincere friendship of the Author, April 20, 1828."

BELA MARSH, Boston

51. Freemasons. Massachusetts. Grand Lodge. Constitutions, compiled by T. M. Harris. Worcester: Isaiah Thomas, 1798. Bound in 1828.

Quarto, 9¼ x 7 inches, red morocco, gilt board edges and turn-ins, marbled endpapers, gilt edges.

The printed ticket of Marsh & Capen, Boston.

PROVENANCE. Presentation inscription tooled on front cover, dated Boston, December, 1828.

REFERENCES. Bela Marsh is listed as bookbinder and stationer in the Boston directories, 1820–1825. Rollo G. Silver, *The Boston Book Trade, 1800–1825* (1949), p. 35.

MOROCCO BINDING, New York

52. Herodotus. Translated from the Greek, By Rev. William Below. 3 vols. New-York: P. P. Berresford, 1828.

12mo, 5⅝ x 3½ inches, red straight-grained morocco, gilt- and blind-tooled, gilt board edges and turn-ins, marbled endpapers, marbled edges.

Illustrated in Andrews, facing p. xvii, and noted on pp. 100–101, but the owner is not identified.

❧ CALF BINDING, New York or Philadelphia

53. John D. Godman. American Natural History. Second Edition. 3 vols. Philadelphia: Kay and Mielkie, 1831.

Octavo, 8¼ x 5⅜ inches, calf gilt- and blind-tooled, gilt board edges and turn-ins, marbled endpapers, gilt edges.

❧ WILSON & NICHOLS, New York

54. The New York Mirror and Ladies Literary Gazette. Edited by George P. Morris. Vol. VIII. New York, 1831.

Large quarto, 12¾ x 10 inches, tan calf, gilt- and blind-tooled, black morocco labels, gilt board edges and turn-ins, marbled endpapers and edges. "Mrs. Emma C[atherine]. Embury" stamped vertically in gilt on front cover.

Binding ascribed to Wilson & Nichols, New York. The first fine early American binding acquired for the collection.

PROVENANCE. Mrs. Emma C. Embury, American author (c. 1806–1863). ". . . When the *New York Mirror* was established she [Mrs. Embury] soon became one of its valued, but unremunerated, contributors" (D.A.B.). Two prose contributions and three poems are checked in the index, probably by her. Three poems signed "Ianthe" [her pseudonym] are also checked. Extra illustrations from other volumes of this publication, mainly of New York buildings, bound in.

❧ HUTCHISON, DWIER & CO., Hartford

55. Album (of engravings and blank pages). 1832 on spine.

Small quarto, 7¼ x 4¾ inches, dark purple, straight-grained morocco, gilt- and blind-tooled, gilt board edges and turn-ins, purple leather doublures with crimson moire flyleaves, edges gilt.

Bound by Hutchison, Dwier & Co., Hartford, with tiny ticket.

PROVENANCE. R. Esmerian, Parke-Bernet Sale, October 13, 1970, Lot 38.

❧ EMBOSSED BINDING, C. A. WELLS, Boston

56. The Token. Edited by S. G. Goodrich. Boston: Charles Bowen, 1836.

12mo, 7¼ x 4½ inches, scarlet morocco, gilt- and blind-tooled, lavender moire endpapers, edges gilt.

"C. A. Wells, Binder, in Boston," blind-tooled at top of spine.

PROVENANCE. Armorial bookplate of Maxwell of Polloc. From the library of Lady Stirling Maxwell.

☙ EMBOSSED BINDING, New York

57. William Cowper. Poems. New-York: Charles Wells, 1840.

12mo, 7⅜ x 4½ inches, original gilt-stamped binding of green roan, gilt board edges, colored endpapers, gilt edges.

☙ EMBOSSED BINDING, S. MOORE, Philadelphia

58. The Gift, a Christmas & New Year's Present for 1842. Philadelphia: Carey and Hart.

Octavo, 7⅝ x 5 inches, cream-colored calf, stamped binding, yellow endpapers, gilt edges.

Signed "S. Moore Binder Phila" at bottom of front board.

PROVENANCE. Inscribed, "To the most amiable Celina Smith, Johnson, R.I., from her friend Benj. F. Latham." Mrs. Mary A. Holloway. Erlene A. Clauss (bookplate).

REFERENCES. Grolier Club, New York, *Catalogue of Ornamental Leather Bookbindings Executed in America Prior to 1850* (New York, 1907), No. 117.

☙ EMBOSSED BINDING, New York

59. The Illuminated Bible. 1600 historical engravings by J. A. Adams, more than 1400 of which are from original designs by J. G. Chapman. New York: Harper & Brothers, 1846.

Large quarto, 13½ x 10 inches, dark blue gilt-stamped morocco, gilt paneled spines, bound as two volumes, gilt board edges and turn-ins, yellow glazed endpapers, gilt edges.

PROVENANCE. Edwin Clark. Abigail Spicer Irving (wife of John Treat Irving). Abbey I. Van Wart (1863).

❧ EMBOSSED BINDING, BENJAMIN BRADLEY, Boston

60. The Ladies Gift. Boston: David P. King, 1850.

12mo, 7½ x 4¾ inches, red morocco, blind- and gilt-stamped, gilt edges.

Embossed on flyleaf, "From Bradley's."

REFERENCES. Joseph W. Rogers, *Bookbinding in America* (1941), pp. 142, 179–180.

❧ PAWSON AND NICHOLSON, Philadelphia

61. Flowers from Cathay [an album of paintings].

Royal quarto, 13 x 11 inches, white calf inlaid with colored morocco, gilt board edges and turn-ins, printed gold endpapers. The outer border is purple morocco, the inner border blue; the initial "F" is yellow, the "C" red and green combined, the flowers and berries are in appropriate colors.

Bound by Pawson and Nicholson, Philadelphia. According to a statement tipped in to the binding, "The 'Flowers from Cathay' were bound by Pawson and Nicholson, March 25th 1864 for Mr. Wister and presented by him to the Sanitary Fair held in Philadelphia, where it was disposed of for $100. The design and tooling were done by James B. Nicholson. April 6th 1888."

PROVENANCE. Calling card of Clarence H. Clark pasted in.

REFERENCES. A sketch of the career of Nicholson, author of *A Manual of the Art of Book Binding* (Philadelphia, 1856), appears in The Grolier Club, New York, *Catalogue of Ornamental Bookbindings . . .* (New York, 1907), No. 127.

1. John Ratcliff

2. John Ratcliff

3. Andrew Bradford's shop

4. Somber Morocco Binding

5.

6. Francis Skinner

7.

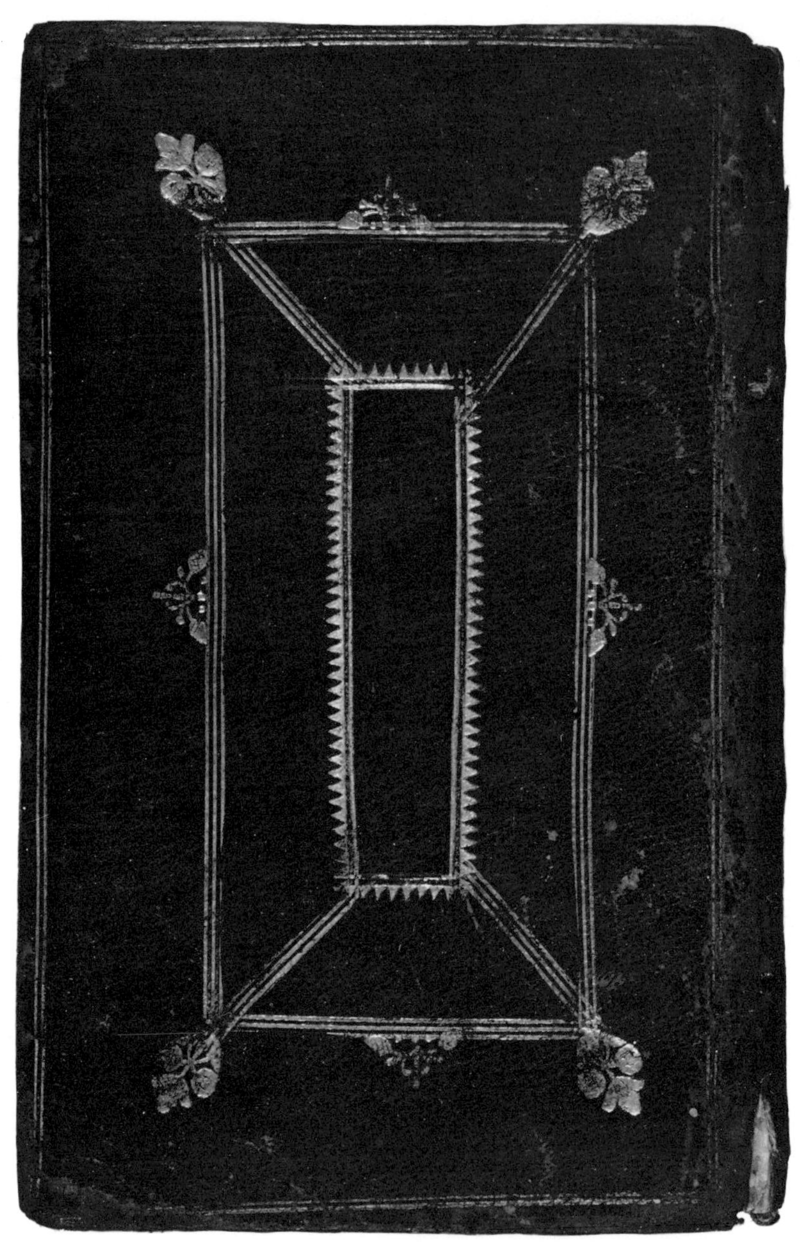

8.

9. Christopher Hoffmann

9A. Andrew Barclay

10. Andrew Barclay

11. William Aikman

12. Robert Aitken's shop

13. Robert Aitken's shop

14. Caleb Buglass

15. Caleb Buglass

Printed and Bound, at Franklin's Head, No. 41, Hanover-Square.

16.

17. James Muir

18. James Muir

19.

20. Henry Bilson Legge

21. James Muir

22. Charles Cleland

23. Henry Bilson Legge

24.

25. Henry Bilson Legge

26. Peter A. Mesier

27. Robert De Silver

28. S. Wadsworth

29. John Roulstone

30. John Roulstone

31. T. Prince

32. John Roulstone

33. John Roulstone

34. J. Katez

35. John Roulstone

36. Wm. W. Potter

37. John Roulstone

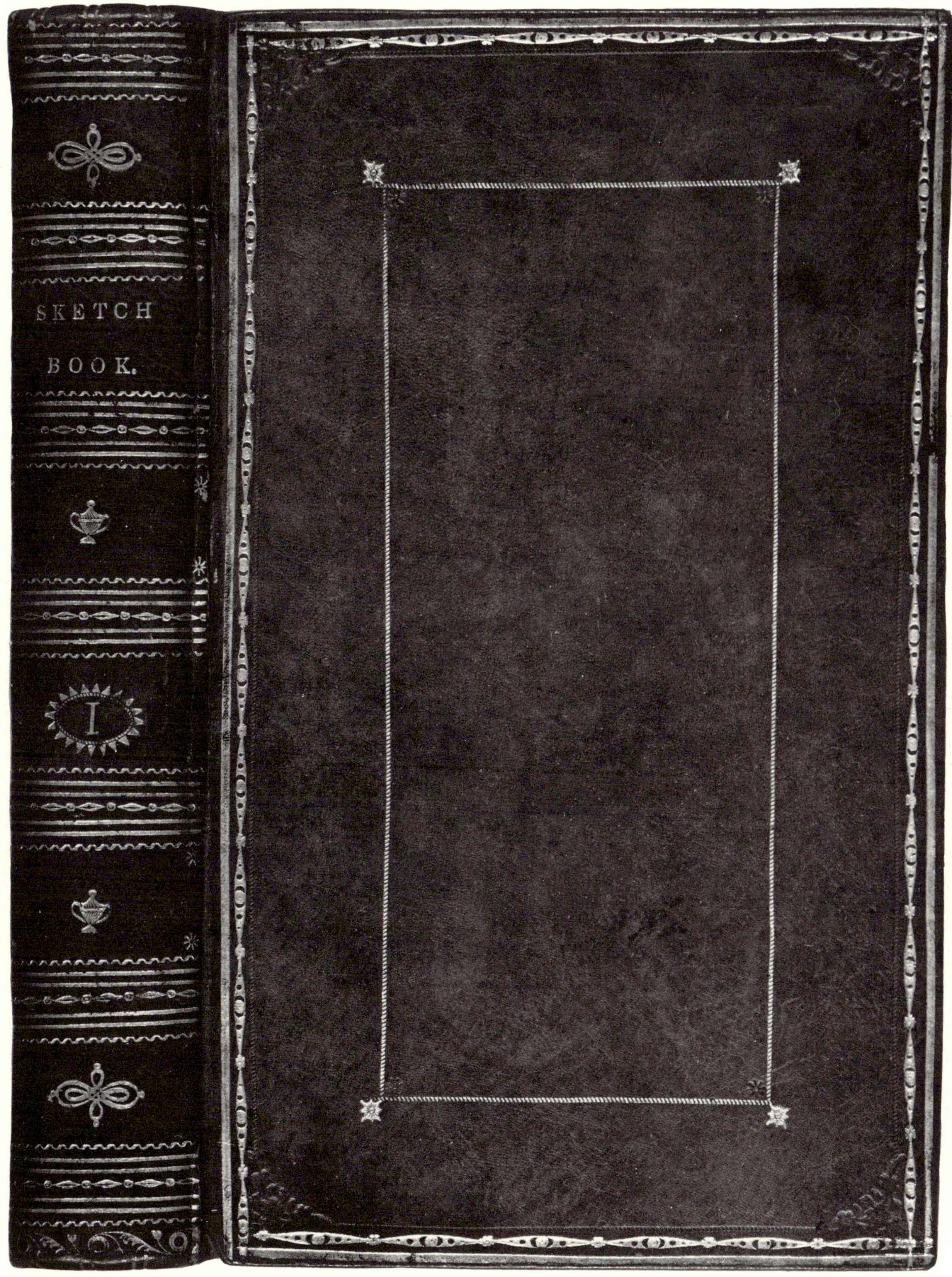

38. Miller & Hutchens

39. Henry I. Megarey

40. T. H. Burnton

41. George Champley

42. John March

43.

44.

45. George Champley

SHAKSPEARE
1
TEMPEST.
TWO GENT. OF VERONA.
MERRY WIVES OF WINDSOR
TWELFTH NIGHT.
MEASURE FOR MEASURE.
MUCH ADO ABOUT NOTHING
MIDSUMMER NIGHT'S DREAM
LOVE'S LABOUR'S LOST.
MERCHANT OF VENICE.
AS YOU LIKE IT.
ALL'S WELL THAT ENDS WE
TAMING OF THE SHREW.
WINTER'S TALE.
COMEDY OF ERRORS.
MACBETH.
KING JOHN.
KING RICHARD II.
KING HENRY IV. PART I.
KING HENRY IV. PART II.
KING HENRY V.

46.

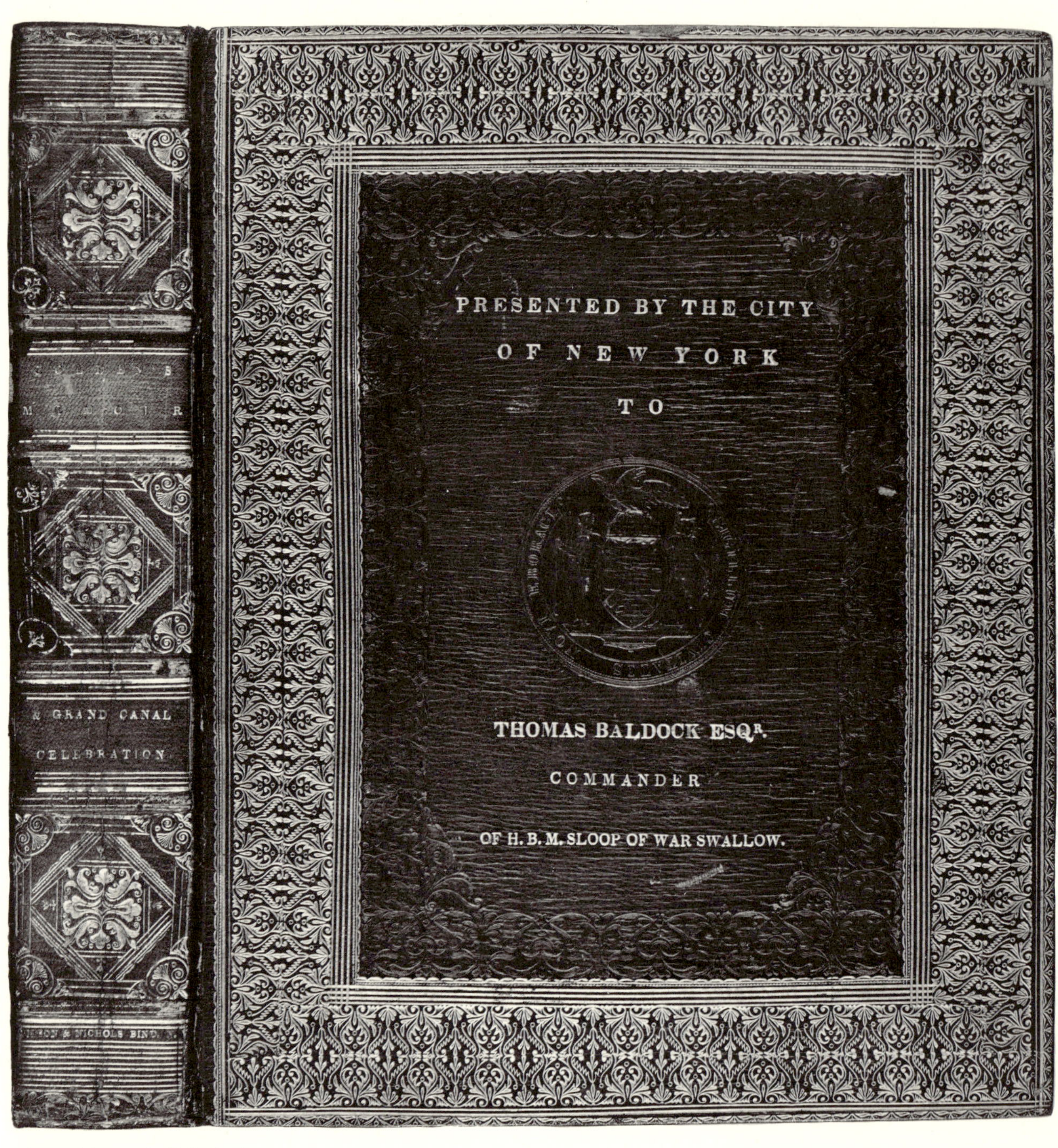

47. Wilson & Nichols

48.

49.

50. Cathedral Panel Binding

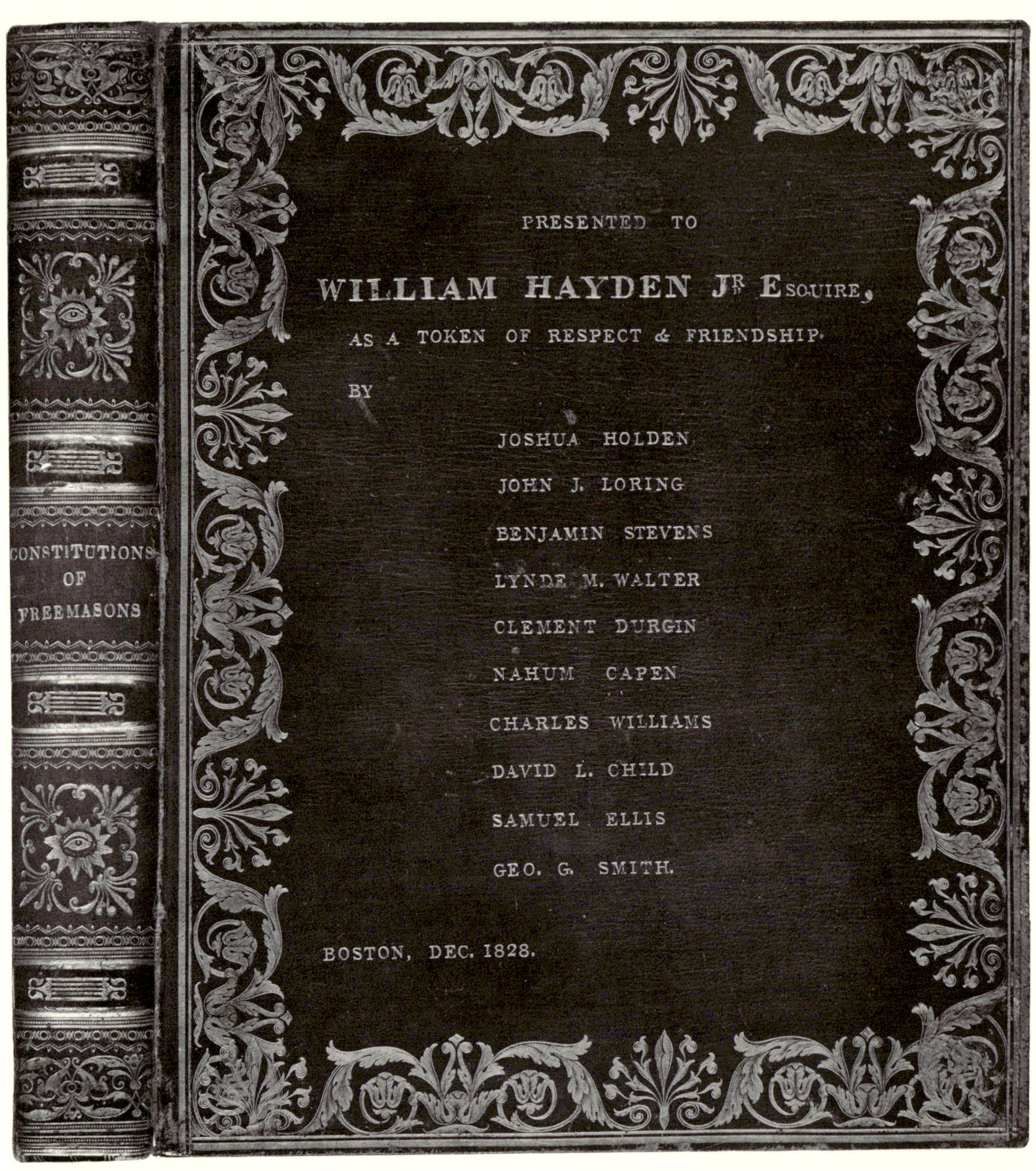

51. Bela Marsh

52.

53. Calf Binding

54. Wilson & Nichols

55. Hutchison, Dwier & Co.

56. Embossed Binding, C. A. Wells

57. Embossed Binding

58. Embossed Binding, S. Moore

59. Embossed Binding

60. Embossed Binding, Benjamin Bradley

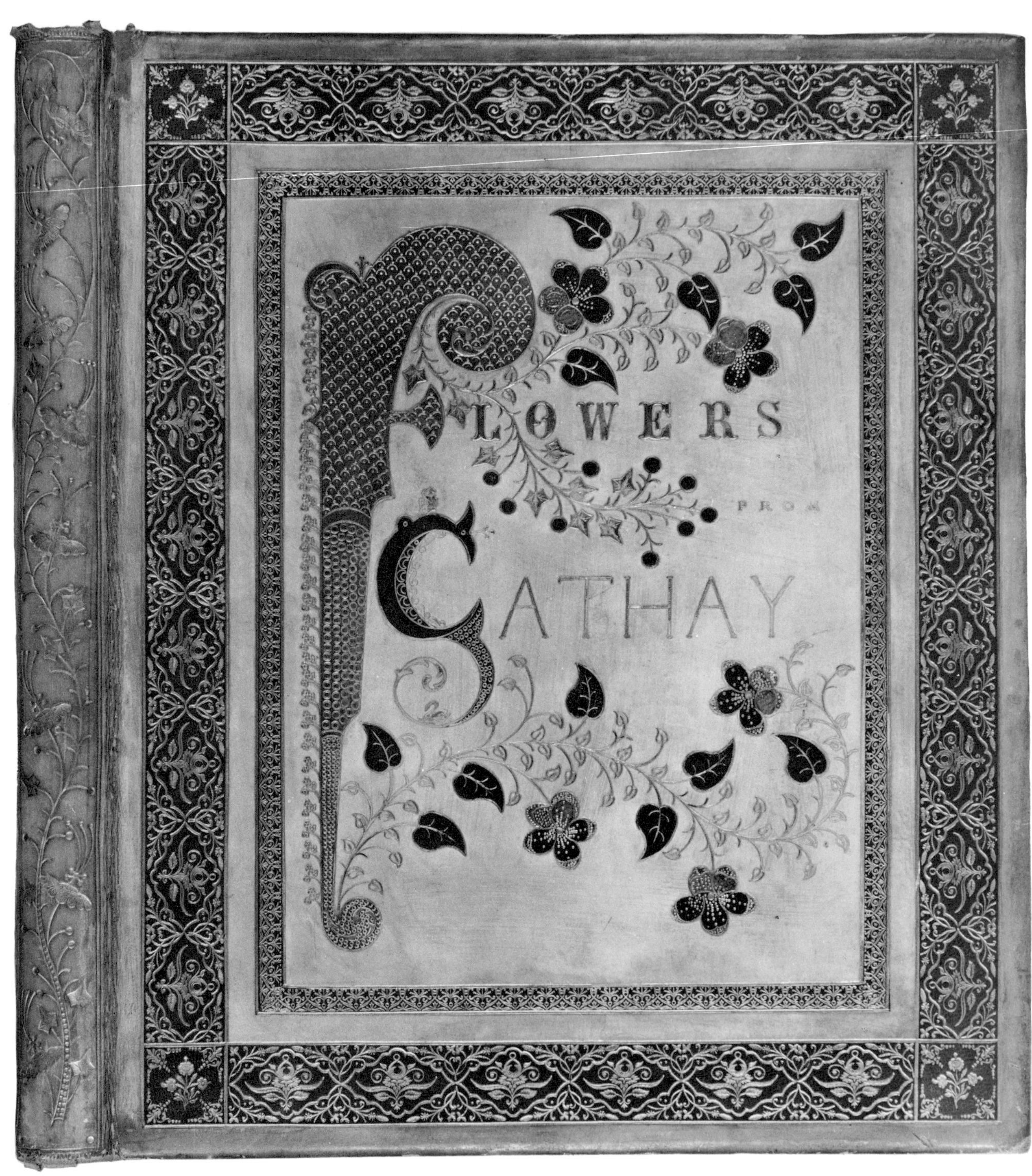

61. Pawson and Nicholson

PRINCIPAL BIBLIOGRAPHICAL CITATIONS

ANDREWS, WILLIAM LORING. *Bibliopegy in the United States and Kindred Subjects.* New York, 1902.

BROWN, H. GLENN AND MAUDE O. *A Directory of Printing, Bookselling, Publishing & Allied Trades in Rhode Island to 1865.* New York 1958.

FRENCH, HANNAH DUSTIN. "The Amazing Career of Andrew Barclay, Scottish Bookbinder of Boston." *Studies in Bibliography. Papers of The Bibliographical Society of the University of Virginia.* Volume 14. Charlottesville, 1961.

FRENCH. "Bound in Boston by Henry B. Legg." *Studies in Bibliography. Papers of The Bibliographical Society of the University of Virginia.* Volume 17. Charlottesville, 1964.

FRENCH. "Caleb Buglass, Binder of the Proposed Book of Common Prayer, Philadelphia, 1786." *Winterthur Portfolio,* Vol. 6. Charlottesville, [1970].

FRENCH. "Early American Bookbinding by Hand." *Bookbinding in America.* Portland, Maine, 1941.

FRENCH. "John Roulstone's Harvard Bindings." *Harvard Library Bulletin.* Cambridge, April, 1970.

GROLIER CLUB. *Catalogue of Ornamental Leather Bookbindings Executed in America Prior to 1850. Exhibited at the Grolier Club, November 7 to 30, 1907.* New York, 1907.

POOR, HENRY WILLIAM. *American Bookbindings in the Library of Henry William Poor. Described by Henri Pène du Bois.* Jamaica, New York, 1903.

SPAWN, WILLMAN AND CAROL. "The Aitken Shop. Identification of an Eighteenth-Century Bindery and Its Tools." *Papers of The Bibliographical Society of America.* Volume 57, Fourth Quarter, New York, 1963.

SPAWN. "Francis Skinner, Bookbinder of Newport. An Eighteenth-Century Craftsman Identified by His Tools." *Winterthur Portfolio*, Vol. 2. Winterthur, Delaware, 1965.

WALTERS ART GALLERY. *The History of Bookbinding 525–1950 A.D. An Exhibition held at the Baltimore Museum of Art, November 12, 1957 to January 12, 1958.* [Arranged by Dorothy Miner.] Baltimore, 1957.

INDEX OF BINDERS

Numbers refer to catalogue entries

INDEX OF PREVIOUS OWNERS

Numbers refer to catalogue entries

INDEX OF AUTHORS

Numbers refer to catalogue entries

Printed by The Stinehour Press
and The Meriden Gravure Company